DISNEY
BEST FRIENDS

pi kids®

phoenix international publications, inc.

Nemo can't wait for his first day of school on the reef! In all the hustle and bustle, can you locate Nemo, his new school chums, their parents, and the teacher, Mr. Ray?

Sheldon

Bob

Bill

Tad

Pearl

Ted

Mr. Ray

Nemo

Rapunzel shares a special moment with Flynn, but unfortunately, he's a man on the run. Under the glowing lanterns, scan the docks for these guards hoping to catch him:

Simba is so excited to be king that his imagination runs away with him! Can you find these royal personalities and objects in Simba's fantasy kingdom?

Simba

his queen

his scout

his herald

his advisor

his crown

his portrait

Mater has lost some shiny new automobile parts in his junkyard. Can you search through all the rusty stuff to help him find them?

this spring

this wheel

this bumper

this tire

this axle

this muffler

Andy's toys travel to lots of interesting places together! Look around this fun-filled room and help Woody, Buzz, and Rex find these new friends:

Twitch

Stretch

Sparks

Big Baby

Chunk

this toy truck

Dory is on a new adventure—searching for her parents! Inside the Marine Life Institute, she meets Hank, an octopus with a missing tentacle. While Hank helps Dory find her way around, look for these aquarium-related things:

whistle

tag

this staff member

diving flippers

megaphone

these pamphlets

Alice, the Mad Hatter, and some other interesting friends are having a cup of tea, or two, or three! Between sips, look around for these mad tea party essentials:

this teapot

this butter knife

jar of jam

this sugar bowl

this teacup

this spoon

King Louie wants to be like you! Search the jungle for Mowgli and these funny monkeys:

Mowgli

this drumming monkey

this swinging monkey

a fanning monkey

this monkey holding bananas

this dancing monkey

Swim back to the reef to find these school-related things:

- stones in the shape of a math problem
- jar of squid ink
- seaweed macramé
- algae map of Australia

Row back to the harbor and count 20 purple lanterns.

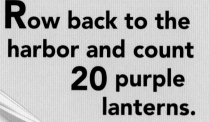

Drift back to Simba's daydream and spot these wacky animals he has envisioned:

- a yellow zebra
- an orange hippo
- a green giraffe
- a purple elephant
- a polka-dotted antelope
- a pink rhino
- a blue ostrich

Mosey back to Mater's junkyard to find these car parts that are in the wrong piles:

- muffler
- tire
- wheel
- bumper
- spring
- axle

Return to the room full of toys and find these little dinos that look up to Rex:

Find your way back to the Marine Life Institute and look for these posters:

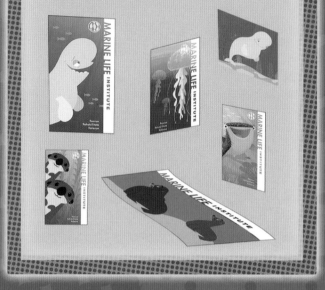

Climb back through the rabbit hole and look for these Wonderland items:

hookah pipe

pocket watch

"Eat Me" candy

pipe

scepter

crown

"Drink Me" bottle

Boogie back to King Louie's ruins and find these jungle plants:

fig tree

mangrove tree

palm leaf

hibiscus flower

violet orchid

banana tree